the Gorp's Gift

Story by
Sherri Chessen

Pictures by
Dale Duncan Johnson

RoundTop
Press

♡ Sherri Chessen

Library of Congress Catalog Card Number: 96-68201

Summary: A poem promoting gun safety for small children.
ISBN 0-9642160-0-0

Printed in Singapore

RoundTop
Press

"I wish I may
I wish I might
Keep the children
safe tonight..."

This book is dedicated
to YOU
with love,

the Gorp

For Carolyn, Jerry & Wennie —
We're thrilled that Gorp
will live with such
wonderful people.
He loves you —
me, too!
Cousin Sherri

What do you think
of a Gorp who would drink
29 bottles of
silvery ink?

A Gorp who would slurrrrp...
a Gorp who would slopppp,
gulping down ink
to the very last

D
  R
    O
      P!

Then... a *shudder!*
A *shiver!*
A *shake!*
and *a quivvvvvver!*
Gorp has some NEWS
he *has* to deliver.

Oops...the ink begins
bubbling
and forming these
words
that TICKLE
Gorp's tummy
like big, bouncy birds.....

so words come out twisted,
some letters are strange,
they're
backwards and
sidewards
and all rearranged.

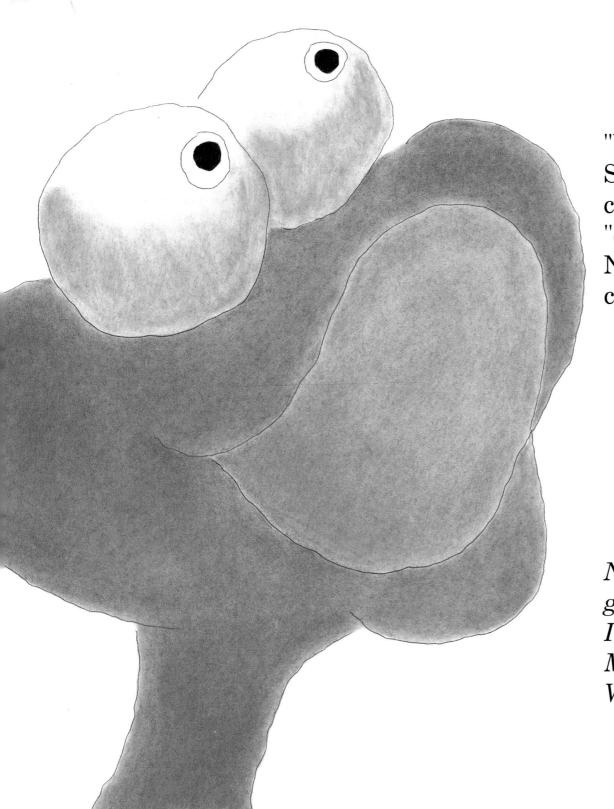

"Watch out for the
SNUG,"
cries Gorp with a shout,
"cuz SAPS with their
NUGS
could wipe us all out!"

*Now what does that mean,
groans gruzzy, old Gorp,
I am NOT making sense!
My words are all
WARPED!*

Gorp MUTTERS!
Gorp SPUTTERS!!
Gorp SQUIRMS!!!
And he SQUIGGLES!!!!

"These words are
important, but
there's too many
WIGGLES!"

*If only they get it
and never forget it.....*

Gorp slides and he sloshes
to the Yinkelbug Hollow...
he flings a
HIGH FIVE
and asks them to follow.

The Yinks get excited,
they love to run races,
so they *zipppppp* after Gorp,
big grins on their faces!

Gorp cuts round a corner,
then *huffffffs*
by a house,
where YoYo McHenry
lives with his spouse.

"It's another Gorp message," says McHenry to mate, "but this one is *jumbled*... the words just aren't *straight* !"

Perhaps all those

L3T13R2

would have some true meaning,
to the well-read
Professor who's as

TALL

as the ceiling!

Professor Tip Tower
is very astute.
His daughter, named
Ivory
is cranky,
but cute.

"Daddy, O Daddy,
what does all that say?
It's not like the Gorp
to misspell in this way!

He's frowning, not clowning,
and starting to droop...
the letters are looking
like ALPHABET SOUP!"

Gorp passes the place
of the groovy
Ms. Lilly,
whose crown, cape and cronies
some simply find silly.

She stands with her valet,
a sweet soul named
Brady,
her chef and her chauffeur,
and her cool cousin
Sadie.

UNGS are
kazooooooming
to the left
and the right,
but ink in Gorp's belly
is _{sinking} from sight.

*If only they get it
and never forget it.....*

Gorp needs a nap.
This running is
work.
He hopes that they
GET IT
and not call him a *jerk*.

When he wakes from his z-z-z-z-'s
Gorp sees quite a sight!
The wind b-l-e-wwww
the letters,
and now...
THEY ARE RIGHT!!!

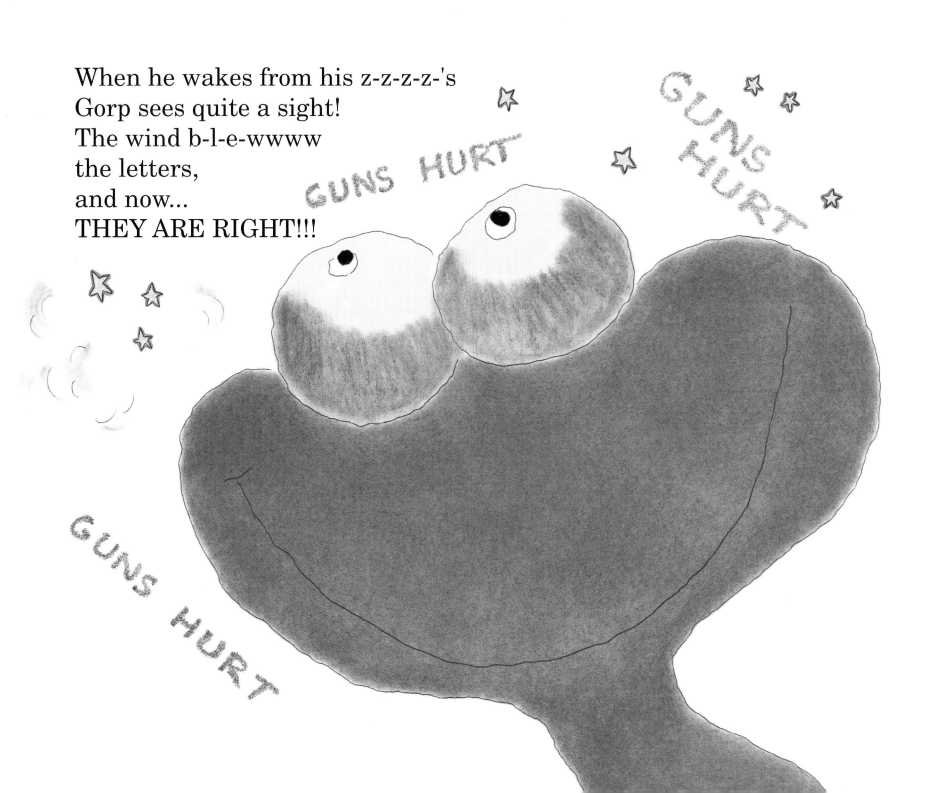

Big Brady, cool Sadie,
the chauffeur and cook
are beaming and gleaming
and screaming...
"OH, LOOK!"

"HOORAY for the wind,"
says Ms. Lilly with glee.
"GUNS HURT
is Gorp's message!!
Makes good sense to me."

"My gift to you all,"
says Gorp with a grin,
"is to make our world SAFER
here's how we'll begin.....

GUNS HURT

GUNS HURT

GUNS HURT

GUNS HURT

GUNS AREN'T FOR KIDS,
so Gorp's number one rule
is NEVER
go near one,
they're simply
NOT COOL!

Real GUNS
can HURT you,
so don't be a
NERD
<u>PLEASE</u> never touch one,
now give me your
WORD!"

"Bye Bye,"
says the Gorp.
"We'll see you real soon...
I'll be on the
rainbow,
the stars,
or the moon!"

I think they get it
I think they do
I think they got it
Hope YOU do, too!

We get it!
We got it!!
We get it!!!
We do!!!!
We promise you Gorp...
NO GUNS for this crew!!!!!

P.S. And they lived...

Here's a PLEDGE
Just for you.
I hope you'll sign...
Gorp does, too!

MY PROMISE TO THE GORP

I promise you, Gorp
and Yinklebugs, too
I promise McHenrys
and the Towers, I DO

I promise Ms. Lilly
her chauffeur and Brady
I promise her chef
and her cool cousin Sadie

I want to be <u>safe</u>
and I promise you now
I WON'T play with GUNS ...
NEVER...NO HOW!

Signed:_____

OFFICIAL STAMP OF THE GORP

Thank you for being a Gorp Gun-Free Kid and remembering that ALL GUNS ARE LOADED!

MY PROMISE TO THE GORP

I promise you, Gorp
and Yinklebugs, too
I promise McHenry's
and the Towers, I DO

I promise Ms. Lilly
her chauffeur and Brady
I promise her chef
and her cool cousin Sadie

I want to be <u>safe</u>
and I promise you now
I WON'T play with GUNS...
NEVER...NO HOW!

Signed: _____